# FREDDY FOX SQUIRREL

OTHER TITLES BY DR. ESCHMEYER

BILLY BASS

TOMMY TROUT

BOBBY BLUEGILL

# FREDDY FOX SQUIRREL

*BY R. W. ESCHMEYER*

*reuben william*

*Designed and Illustrated by*
ROY K. WILLS

PUBLISHED BY FISHERMAN PRESS, INC., OXFORD, OHIO

SECOND EDITION

*T his is the
true-to-life story
of a fox squirrel
and how he lived*

ONE cold March morning Farmer Smith took down the "No Hunting" signs which had been nailed to the fence posts around his farm. This didn't mean that Farmer Smith was going to let people hunt squirrels in his wood lot or rabbits in his fields. He was taking the signs down because the hunting season had ended for another **year.**

The signs weren't needed now. Farmer Smith took them to his tool shed, where he would repaint them. In the fall he would put them back on the fence posts, warning people not to hunt on his farm.

Farmer Smith never went hunting himself. He liked his fox squirrels and rabbits. He didn't want anyone to kill them.

The squirrels lived in Farmer Smith's wood lot, which was surrounded by pasture land. The squirrels almost never entered the pasture. There were no trees in the pasture for the squirrels to climb in, and there was no food for them to eat.

Farmer Smith was proud of his wood lot. It

was about as big as four city blocks. Most of the trees were oaks. Some were white oaks and some were black oaks. Of course, the white oak isn't really white, and the black oak isn't really black, but the bark on the white oak is much lighter than that on the black oak.

When Farmer Smith bought the farm years ago, there were many trees in the wood lot which would never be good for lumber. Some of the trees were too crooked, and some which were straight were still not good enough for making boards. Each fall and winter Farmer Smith had cut down a few of these trees and sawed them into pieces for his fireplace. He also sold some of the wood to people in the city for use in their fireplaces.

Now there were no more hickory or walnut trees left in the wood lot. Soon now Farmer Smith would cut down the biggest

oaks and take them to the sawmill. Here they would be sawed into boards.

Scattered around the edge of the wood lot were eight big white oak trees. They were very big, and their branches spread out over the pasture beyond the fence. In summer the cows rested in the shade of these branches. Farmer Smith often thought of cutting down these eight big trees for fireplace wood. He knew that they would not be good for lumber because the branches were big and because each trunk had a hole in it. The holes had been formed years ago where branches broke from the trees. The squirrels gnawed the bark away each year so it could not cover the holes.

Farmer Smith didn't cut these trees. He liked the wild animals, and he knew that the squirrels built nests in these trees. For this reason they were called den trees. The hole high in each trunk was big enough for a fox squirrel to enter but too small for an opossum or a raccoon. The big white oaks were the homes of the squirrels.

As Farmer Smith looked at one of the big den trees, a fox squirrel surprised him by appearing at the opening. She scampered down the tree trunk and onto the snow-covered ground. She stopped and sniffed. Then she moved ahead, stopping and sniffing every once in a while. Suddenly she began to dig into the snow with her front feet. Then she started to dig in the ground beneath the snow. She found the acorn that

she had smelled and was soon eating it. She had sharp claws and sharp teeth and knew how to use them. The acorn she ate was one of many which the squirrels had buried in the ground during the fall. The squirrel dug a few acorns each day and ate them.

Though Farmer Smith didn't know it, this mother squirrel had three young ones in her nest in the big white oak tree. They were only a day old. They didn't look like squirrels. They had no bushy tails. In fact, they had no fur at all, and their eyes were still closed.

One of these three helpless little squirrels was Freddy. The other two were his sisters.

In time Farmer Smith's "No Hunting" signs, the pasture, and the cutting down of nearly all the trees other than the oaks would all mean something very important to Freddy. We'll tell you about it later.

# FREDDY GROWS

WHEN Freddy was very small, he spent most of his time sleeping. Even though he had no fur coat, Freddy was warm because the nest in the tree was lined with oak leaves. The strong March winds didn't bother him at all.

Freddy's claws were sharp even when he was very young. He would need good sharp claws to hold him when he climbed up and down the tree trunks. He would need them, too, so that he could bury acorns and nuts in the fall and uncover them again in the winter.

When Freddy was a week old, some hair began to grow on his back. A few weeks later he was partly covered with brown fur. His tail began to look less like the tail of a mouse and more like the bushy tail of a grown-up fox squirrel. He was fully a month old when he first started to open his eyes. Each day he could see a little better. One day Freddy climbed to the opening in his nest. The bright sunlight hurt his eyes for a little while, but soon he enjoyed his trips to the nest-opening high in the white oak tree. Then he began to climb around on the limb of the tree near his nest. He nearly fell, but his sharp claws dug into the bark and held him there. Soon he felt quite safe in the tree.

A little later Freddy had another new experience. He had been climbing around on the tree each day for a week or more, but this time he left

the tree and scampered around on the ground. Soon he went back to the white oak, where he felt more at home. Each day he ventured a little farther from the den tree. Sometimes he climbed up some of the other trees near his home. Once he even leaped from the

branch of one tree to the branch of another tree which was close by.

One evening Freddy was out later than usual. It was beginning to get dark. Suddenly a big bird flew near him. Freddy scampered into his den just as the bird was ready to catch him. The big bird was a great horned owl. The owl liked to eat squirrels, but it rarely caught them even though it often sat in a den tree.

Owls sleep during the day and hunt for food after dark. Fox squirrels eat and play during the day, but they spend their nights sleeping in the den trees and leaf nests. That is why owls rarely catch fox squirrels.

Freddy didn't stay out late in the evenings after his narrow escape from the big bird. He often heard the owl hoot as it sat in a nearby tree, but he never saw it again. Whenever the owl was awake, Freddy was asleep, safe in his den tree.

As he grew older, Freddy ate the buds on some of the limbs. One day he ate an acorn. He liked it. Soon he was eating acorns every day. They were his favorite food. Of course, there wasn't much else for him to eat. The tall, straight trees were covered with leaves. These leaves kept the

sunlight from reaching the ground so that there were few small bushes in the wood lot. The pasture around the woods was well supplied with grass and clover. A rabbit would have found plenty to eat in the pasture, but squirrels don't eat grass or clover. They eat acorns and other nuts and also the seeds and small twigs of some of the trees and bushes.

Freddy was very sure-footed when he scampered in the trees, but once when he was about to cut a twig, he fell to the ground. This frightened Freddy, but the fall didn't hurt him. Soon he was cutting more twigs.

By late July Freddy was almost a full-grown squirrel. He still slept in the den where he was born, but he spent the days scampering around

on the ground and climbing and jumping from tree to tree. Of course, he spent much of the time hunting for food. Sometimes he would rest in a leaf nest, which had been built by another fox squirrel. These leaf nests were very different from the nest in which he was born.

The leaf nests were built of twigs and leaves in the branches of a tall oak tree. They weren't

inside the trunk of the tree but right out where you could see them. The leaf nests were made by the mother squirrels. Often a mother squirrel would build several of them.

One evening as Freddy returned to the big white oak tree to sleep in the nest where he had been born, his mother wouldn't let him come in. She chased his two sisters away, too. So they slept in the leaf nests in nearby trees.

The next day she chased them away again. They saw that they weren't welcome and never returned to the den. They didn't know, of course, that they would soon have two new sisters and a brother. The nest wouldn't be big enough for all of the family, so the mother simply didn't let the other children use it.

Freddy and his sisters didn't feel badly. They didn't mind being chased away. Mother squirrels always chase their children away when they are old enough to take care of themselves.

Freddy lived in the nearby trees and slept in several of the leaf nests high in these trees. These nests sheltered him from the rain and from the great horned owl. He was contented.

# HUNGER

IN September and October Freddy was a very busy squirrel. The other squirrels in the wood lot were all busy, too. They spent a part of each day eating acorns, of course, but they also began to bury some in the ground. They used their claws to dig a hole and to cover it. You would think that they would drop several acorns in each hole, but they placed only one acorn in each.

The oak trees had only a small crop of acorns this fall, but there were plenty for the squirrels to eat and some for them to store in the ground for their winter food.

Freddy's cousin, the red squirrel, hid his winter supply of acorns in hollow trees where he could find them later. There were no red squirrels in Farmer Smith's wood lot, but even if they had been there and if Freddy had watched them store their food, he still would have buried the acorns in the

ground, just as the other fox squirrels did. Each kind of animal has its own way of doing things.

Freddy couldn't remember where he buried each acorn. He didn't even try to remember where he put them. He and the other fox squirrels would find most of them again later. They had a very keen sense of smell. Even with some snow on the ground they would be able to smell where the acorns were hidden. Freddy would eat some of the acorns which he buried himself and some of those stored in the ground by the other fox squirrels.

Farmer Smith was harvesting a crop, too. In his cornfield near the wood lot a corn picker, pulled by a tractor, was tearing the ears of corn from the stalks and dropping them into a wagon. When he had finished with the harvesting, he turned his pigs loose in the field. They ate the corn which the machine didn't pick. The stalks were all flat on the ground. Now there wasn't any food for the squirrels in this cornfield, and the stalks would no longer protect any squirrels from the hawks and other enemies.

In the fall fox squirrels often take long trips to look for new homes. But Freddy and his sisters stayed in Farmer Smith's wood lot. They didn't want to travel through the open pasture or the bare cornfield. A hawk, dog, or fox might find them. They stayed in the wood lot and buried acorns. The squirrels would never find all of the acorns they buried. Some would grow to be as big as the tree in which Freddy and his sisters were born.

Most of the acorns were buried by late October. Since the crop of acorns had been poor this fall, the supply placed in the ground by the squirrels was not enough to feed all of them in the wood lot during the following winter. Freddy didn't know that he would be hungry later. At the moment he had plenty to eat.

Once while Freddy was burying an acorn, a squirrel barked in another part of the wood lot. Freddy stood on his hind legs and looked and listened. The barking told Freddy to be on the lookout for something unusual.

The barking of a fox squirrel is very different from the barking of a dog. Usually a fox squirrel barks when he is excited. When other fox squirrels barked, Freddy always looked around very carefully because it often meant that some enemy might be going through the woods. It might be a hawk or a dog.

As Freddy looked, he saw a rabbit running toward him as fast as the rabbit could run. Freddy  ran up a tree trunk and watched. Soon he saw why the rabbit was running so fast. A red fox was chasing the rabbit. When Freddy saw the fox, he did a very unusual thing. In the excitement he barked, too. This was the first time he had ever barked though he had often made small

noises while playing. In the future he would often bark.

On the day before the hunting season began, Farmer Smith placed his "No Hunting" signs around his farm. Freddy wasn't interested in the signs. He couldn't read them. He didn't know that these signs were placed on the fence posts partly for his benefit. The next morning Freddy could hear sharp cracking noises in the wood lots on some of the neighboring farms. Sometimes there would also be a loud booming noise. It was the opening day of the squirrel hunting season. Men were sitting quietly on stumps or on the ground near den trees. The loud noises were the sounds of their guns. Each such noise meant that someone had seen another squirrel and had shot at it. The booming sounds were made by hunters who used shotguns to kill the squirrels. Most of the hunters were using rifles. They missed more of the squirrels because a rifle fires only one shot instead of the dozens of small shot fired from a shotgun. The hunters who used rifles were more interested in the skill of shooting. They enjoyed the trip even though they shot fewer squirrels.

The loud noises meant nothing to Freddy. He knew nothing about guns. The noises were far away. There were no loud noises in Farmer Smith's wood lot.

Freddy was very busy, though. He was no longer burying acorns in the ground. There were no more acorns to bury. He was digging them up and eating them. There was a light snow on the ground, but this didn't bother the squirrels. They dug through it. For several weeks Freddy was able to find enough food. Then the acorns became scarce. Often he hunted a long time to find even one. Then one day he found none at all. He was hungry when he went to bed that night.

The next day he did something unusual. After he hunted for acorns for a while and found none, he traveled across the open pasture to a cornfield

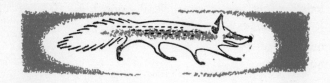

where the farmer had cut his corn by hand and placed it in shocks. It was a long trip through the pasture. Of course, Freddy didn't mind the distance; he could travel for several miles. He worried, though, all the while he traveled. We shouldn't say that he worried, because squirrels probably don't worry. But he was afraid and felt very uneasy. He ran fast, stopping every few minutes to see if any enemies were near.

If Farmer Smith had left some trees growing along his fences, Freddy would have followed one of the fence lines. But Farmer Smith knew that there would be less grass and clover under the trees. He had cut them so that he would have a little more pasture. Freddy could get to the corn-field only by getting far away from trees.

A squirrel seldom travels where there are no trees close to him. On the open pasture land a number of animals can run faster than a squirrel can. A fox or a dog might catch the squirrel. A

22

hawk might swoop down and catch him. Few of Freddy's enemies could catch him in the wood lot, but any of several kinds of enemies might catch him in the pasture.

Freddy was very lucky. None of his enemies saw him. In the field the corn was standing in shocks. Freddy soon pulled the husk from an ear of corn and started eating. He was very hungry. He ate and ate. He ate only the rich oily center from each kernel. Ordinarily Freddy would have carried the ear of corn to the base of a tree. Then he would scamper to safety if an enemy appeared. But there were no trees close, so he ate his meal in the cornfield. Later he began to hunt for a place to take a long nap. He could have slept in one of the shocks of corn, but he didn't feel at home there. He saw a tree in the distance. It

wasn't a very big tree, and it stood all alone. Freddy started to run toward it.

In Farmer Smith's wood lot Freddy had a good home. In fact, he had several good homes. But when the acorn crop was poor, there wasn't enough food to keep all the squirrels fed during the winter. The beech trees were filled with beechnuts this year. The hickory and walnut trees produced many nuts, too. This hadn't helped Freddy because the trees in Farmer Smith's wood lot were nearly all oaks. Here in the cornfield Freddy had plenty of food, but he had no place to sleep. A good home isn't very helpful unless there is food nearby, and food isn't very helpful unless a good home can be found not far away. Of course, a squirrel is willing to travel a mile or more to get food. But he likes to travel in or near the woods, not in the open pasture.

As Freddy ran toward the tree, he heard a noise coming nearer. He ran as fast as he could, but the animal making the noise was gaining. It was Farmer Smith's dog. He barked as he ran. He had seen Freddy, and he had tried to catch him. Of course, if the dog had caught him, that would have been the end of our squirrel.

Freddy reached the tree just as the dog was about to catch him. It was a small tree, but Freddy scampered to the top of it. The dog barked and barked, but he couldn't reach the squirrel. Freddy sat there shaking with fright. After a long while the dog started running down the field, hoping to find a rabbit. Now Freddy knew he was safe, but he spent the night in the small tree.

Freddy didn't go back to that cornfield. He didn't want to meet that dog again. Freddy went to a different cornfield. Soon he had eaten another good meal. He traveled for several miles that day. Sometimes he was near the trees, and several times he ran through fields and pastures. None of his enemies saw him this time. Toward evening he finally reached a big oak tree in a wood lot. He climbed into the tree and found a big leaf nest. It was empty. Soon Freddy was in the leaf nest sleeping soundly.

In Farmer Smith's wood lot far away, one of Freddy's sisters had just died of starvation. His other sister was weak and just about to die of a disease. The squirrels in Farmer Smith's wood lot had fine homes. They were safe from their enemies and from the hunters. But they were starving because the oak trees hadn't produced many acorns. There had been crops of beechnuts and hickory nuts, but the beech and hickory trees were far away. Big pastures separated them from the wood lot.

On the evening when Freddy found his new home, Farmer Smith sat by his fireplace. He had just eaten a big chicken dinner. He happened to be thinking about his wood lot. He was glad that he hadn't cut the den trees, because he wanted the squirrels in his wood lot to have good homes. He didn't want hunters to kill any of them. Farmer Smith enjoyed seeing them and hearing them. Poor Farmer Smith didn't know that at this very moment many of his squirrels were starving.

# FREDDY'S NEW HOME

 AFTER a long night's sleep in the leaf nest Freddy climbed down the tree trunk and hunted for breakfast. Soon he smelled food. It didn't smell like an acorn, but that didn't bother Freddy. He knew it would be good to eat. He dug into the ground and soon had the food in his paws. It was a big hickory nut. Freddy had never seen one before, but he knew exactly what to do with it. He held the nut in his paws as his sharp teeth chiseled away the shell. He liked this new kind of food.

There were very few acorns in the wood lot. The oak trees hadn't produced many acorns during the summer. Even without the acorns, though, there was plenty of food. Other squirrels had buried many hickory nuts, walnuts, and beechnuts. Freddy had

29

both food and shelter in his new home. He liked it.

Freddy's new home was owned by Joe's father. Joe was a junior in high school. During the summer he helped his father with the farming. Of course, he also helped in the evenings and on week ends during the school year. Both Joe and his father liked to hunt squirrels and rabbits. This meant that Freddy might serve as dinner for Joe some day.

Mr. Miller, Joe's father, was a good farmer. He knew that the land would raise good crops only if he kept the topsoil on his fields. He planted trees on the steep slopes, and along the gullies and the creek to keep the soil from washing away. The farm had a big wood lot, of course, but there were many other patches of trees. Walnut trees grew

along some of the fences. In the smaller patches and around the big wood lot, there were many kinds of trees. The hickory, walnut, beech, and oak trees all furnished good food for the squirrels. Some of the white oaks and beech trees were fine den trees. In these trees the mother squirrels built their nests and raised their young.

Little by little Freddy examined the wood lot and the many patches of trees. He didn't need to run through the pasture where a hawk or a fox or a dog might catch him. He followed the tree-lined fence rows. There was some food buried in the ground at each of the patches of trees, and Freddy always found a leaf nest or a den tree to sleep in at night. Many other squirrels lived on Mr. Miller's farm, but all of them had enough to eat. They were all contented.

Freddy soon began to feel at home in his new wood lot. The snow began to melt. Buds and leaves began to appear on the trees. All during the spring and summer the squirrels spent most of the time eating and sleeping.

In many of the den trees small squirrels began to look out of the openings of their nests. Soon they would be climbing around on the trees. Later they would scamper through the wood lot. During early fall there would be more young squirrels. A few nests had only one little squirrel in them, but in others there were as many as five. All of these squirrels needed food. Soon Freddy and the other fox squirrels would be busy filling their "cupboard." Their "cupboard" was the ground under the trees.

# HARVEST TIME

W HEN the frosts came in the fall and the leaves were turning color, Mr. Miller was busy harvesting his corn. In the wood lot and in the many patches of trees on the farm the fox squirrels were busy, too. They dug holes in the ground with their sharp claws. The holes weren't very deep. Each time a hole was dug, an acorn or a nut was dropped into it, and the hole was covered with soil. During the long fall each fox squirrel buried many dozens of acorns and nuts.

This buried food belonged to all the squirrels. If each squirrel buried a supply of winter food

only for himself, some of the young squirrels would starve. Those which were born in late summer or early fall still weren't big enough to help fill the "cupboard."

34

Joe and his father often took walks through the woods on Sunday afternoons. They would look at the oak trees and at the hickory and other nut trees. Freddy often saw them walk through the woods. He watched them as they looked at the trees. He didn't know why they took these walks. He didn't care.

Mr. Miller and Joe had read several booklets about the fox squirrel. They had also talked with the state game man about squirrels. They learned that an acre of good wood lot could furnish food for about one squirrel. When food was plentiful, the wood lot would furnish food for more than one squirrel to the acre, but when food was scarce, the acorns and nuts would feed fewer squirrels.

Altogether the Miller farm had about thirty acres of trees. Most of these were in the wood lot, but some were along the fence rows and some were on the steep slopes and along the gullies. The state game man had told Mr. Miller that his patches of woods were ideal for fox squirrels. There were many den trees and many nut trees.

We're glad Freddy couldn't understand what Joe and his father were saying one fall day after a long walk. He might have worried if he had understood what they said.

Here is what Mr. Miller was saying to Joe: "The walnut crop is small this year, but the oak, hickory and beech trees have all produced well. The squirrels will have plenty of food this winter. I guess there are about thirty squirrels in our thirty acres of woods. Suppose we harvest about fifteen of them?"

"Let's take only twelve," said Joe. His father agreed. They would enjoy harvesting this crop.

The Millers had certain rules for harvesting the squirrel crop. They and their friends would take only twelve, and each person could take no more than two in one day. They could use only rifles. The game laws permitted them to take five each day, but the Millers would not take this many.

When the hunting season opened, Joe sat quietly on a stump near a big white oak tree. It was still early morning. The sun was a big yellow ball on the horizon. Joe sat very still.

Freddy had been sleeping all night. He was hungry now. He left the den where he spent the night and started moving along the tree trunk. As Freddy ran, Joe moved his arm. He was excited. Freddy hadn't seen Joe, but he saw something move. He stopped to see what was moving on the stump. Just as Freddy stopped, something hit the trunk of the tree right near his nose. There was a loud noise, too. It surprised him so much that he fell to the ground and scampered away as fast as he could run. Then he climbed up another tree as fast as he could and crawled into a leaf nest. He

stayed there all day and slept there that night. The fall hadn't hurt Freddy at all, but he was frightened.

If Joe's rifle shot had been an inch lower, Freddy would have been in the Miller's home that evening. He would have been on a platter on the dining room table!

Joe didn't mind seeing Freddy run away. He knew that there were many squirrels in the woods and that he would have more chances to shoot his rifle.

There were more loud noises in the woods. Freddy could hear them. By noon there were no more noises in Mr. Miller's woods, but Freddy could still hear some of them in the distance. Joe and his father each had two squirrels in their hunting coats. They never shot more than two in one day. They were walking home now.

A chart was tacked on the back porch of Joe's home. Three names were on the chart. They were "Joe," "Dad," and "Friends." When Joe and his father returned to the house, they placed two marks behind each of the first two names.

For several weeks Freddy heard the loud noises nearly every day. He always found a few acorns and then scampered back to his leaf nest. One day there were no more loud noises. The next day was a quiet one, too. Soon Freddy forgot about his unhappy experience. He could still hear sharp

noises and loud "booms" in the other wood lots, but these were far away and he didn't mind them. There was plenty of food, and Freddy was happy.

On the chart on Mr. Miller's back porch there were five marks behind Joe's name, four behind the word "Dad," and three behind the word "Friends." The twelve squirrels had been harvested. That ended the squirrel season on the Miller farm. Joe would still visit the woods and sit quietly on a stump. He would watch the squirrels. His rifle was in a closet at home. He enjoyed just watching the squirrels.

One day as Freddy sat on a limb enjoying the sunshine, Joe suddenly jumped from a nearby stump and cried, "Boom!" Freddy ran away as fast as he could run. Joe laughed as he watched Freddy run. Freddy didn't know that Joe was simply having fun and that he was not in danger.

# ANOTHER FALL

FREDDY and the other squirrels had plenty to eat that winter and during the next spring and summer. Soon the busy fall season arrived. The squirrels hurried about burying the winter supply of food. Some of the squirrels wandered away from the Millers' farm, while others moved in from nearby. Freddy stayed. He liked the wood lot. Joe and his father made their usual Sunday afternoon visits to the woods. If Freddy could have understood what they were saying this time, he really would have been worried.

Here is what Mr. Miller was saying to Joe: "The nut trees have given a fairly good crop again this year, but the acorn crop is light. We have only about half the acorns we had last year. There are many more leaf nests this year so we also have more squirrels. I would guess that there are about forty of them. I think we should take twenty-five this year. Then there will be food enough for the other fifteen or so squirrels."

Joe agreed that they should take twenty-five squirrels. Otherwise they might starve during the winter because food was less plentiful this year. Sometimes the trees have many nuts or acorns, but on other years the crop is smaller.

The twenty-five squirrels would give Joe, his father, and their friends many days of hunting. These would be pleasant days on the Miller farm. Mrs. Miller enjoyed the hunting season, too, because she liked to eat squirrels. Sometimes she baked them, and sometimes she fried them. Once she made squirrel pie.

On opening day Joe, his father, and two friends were in the wood lot shortly after daylight. Soon Freddy heard the crack of a rifle shot. He didn't like that kind of noise. Perhaps it reminded him of his experience of a year ago. Fortunately, the shot happened to be fired at another squirrel, not at Freddy.

In a few hours there was no more shooting in the Millers' woods. The four hunters had each shot two squirrels. That was the limit on the Miller farm. In other wood lots the men were still shooting. Of course, there was no shooting in the wood lot where Freddy was born. Farmer Smith's "No Hunting" signs were back on the fence posts.

Late in the day Freddy left the leaf nest and

looked around. He saw no one. He scampered
to the ground and ate several acorns. Then he
went back to the leaf nest. Really, he was not in
danger. The four hunters were sitting around Mr.
Miller's fireplace talking about hunting and about
the woods. They were looking forward to a dinner
of fried squirrel. There would be no more shooting
that day on Mr. Miller's farm.

Joe spent many hours in the woods hunting
squirrels. Sometimes he shot two, and sometimes
he got only one. Finally the chart on the back
porch showed that another squirrel hunting season
had ended. The twenty-five squirrels had been

taken. There were eight marks behind Joe's name and seven behind the word "Dad." The other ten marks were behind the word "Friends."

Soon after the hunting season ended, the snow began to fall. Freddy and the other fox squirrels found plenty of nests. They also found plenty of food even though the oaks hadn't produced many acorns that year. There were only about fifteen squirrels in the woods, and the "cupboard" would take care of their needs. The squirrels were fat and well fed.

In the wood lot where Freddy was born, the fox squirrels were unhappy. Here, too, the acorn crop had been a poor one. There was no other food because Farmer Smith had cut down all the trees except the white oaks and the black oaks. The squirrels had an empty "cupboard" by the middle of the winter. Some were starving to death. The others were always hungry. Most of them died because there wasn't enough food.

Freddy had forgotten all about the wood lot where he was born. He forgot about the time when Mr. Smith's dog almost caught him. He had a good home and plenty of food, and he was happy.

Each morning Freddy would look out of the nest he had slept in. If it was cold, or if it was snowing hard or sleeting, he simply curled up in the nest and took another long snooze. He was fat and didn't need food every day. Of course, when the weather was nice, he ran around in the snow and dug up some of the nuts and acorns. He didn't know that he was happy and contented only because Joe and his father liked the squirrels and knew how to manage them. If the Millers hadn't taken part of the squirrel crop during the hunting season, Freddy would be starving, too.

Instead of shooting some of the squirrels, Joe and his father might have hauled several loads of corn to the woods. But they needed the corn for other things. They fed it to the hogs. When these hogs were big and fat, Joe and his father sold them. This is how they earned the money they needed to buy their food, their car, and the many other things which people need. We couldn't expect them to feed their corn to the squirrels when they needed it for more important things.

Joe and his father left other nut trees on the farm as well as the white oaks and the black oaks. Each fall they examined the crop of nuts and acorns to see how many squirrels could be fed by this crop. Then they hunted just enough squirrels so that the remaining ones would have enough to eat. They enjoyed hunting the squirrels, and they enjoyed eating them. They also enjoyed knowing that the squirrels which spent the winter on their farm would have good homes and all the food they needed.

Freddy didn't know about all these things. When the weather was nice, he scampered about in the snow and dug up all the nuts and acorns he wanted. When the weather was bad, he went back to bed. Freddy enjoyed sleeping. In fact, he was a bit lazy.

# ABOUT THE AUTHOR

Dr. R. W. Eschmeyer, a professional conservationist for more than twenty years, received his formal training at Heidelberg College, the University of Michigan, and Indiana University. His specialty is fish conservation. The fox squirrel manuscript was checked by four leading wildlife conservationists before the author released it for publication. The four authorities who checked the manuscript are: Dr. Durward L. Allen, U. S. Fish and Wildlife Service; Dr. Charles A. Dambach, Ohio Division of Wildlife; Mr. Harry D. Ruhl, Michigan Department of Conservation; and Dr. Joseph P. Linduska, U. S. Fish and Wildlife Service.

AB